REFRIGERANT USAGE CERTIFICATION

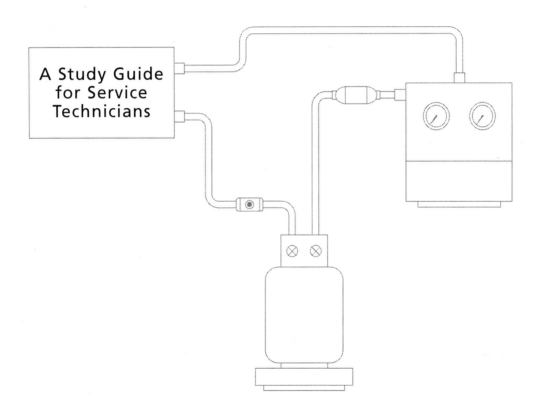

A Study Guide
for Service
Technicians

The HVACR Training Authority

ISBN-13: 978-1-61607-129-5
ISBN-10: 1-61607-129-X

TABLE OF CONTENTS

SECTION 1: CORE

SECTION 2: SMALL APPLIANCES

SECTION 3: HIGH-PRESSURE SYSTEMS

SECTION 4: LOW-PRESSURE SYSTEMS

ACKNOWLEDGEMENTS

RSES extends its thanks to the following individuals for their help in reviewing and updating the contents of this book:

- Kenneth Bachner, CMS

- Robb Isaacs, CMS

- Irvin Moeller, CMS

- Frank Prah, CMS

- Loren "Shorty" Shuck, CMS

- Tim Gioe

- Renee Tomlinson

On September 30, 1993, RSES was approved by the U.S. Environmental Protection Agency (EPA) to conduct technician certification testing per EPA regulations. This approval was in accordance with Section 608 of the Clean Air Act Amendments of 1990. The effective date of approval was October 15, 1993.

Examinations are constructed from an EPA-supplied bank of questions. The tests, which are closed-book exams, consist of four groups of questions. The candidate must receive a passing grade (18 correct out of 25 questions, or 70%) on each of the four question groups (Core, Type I, Type II, Type III) pertaining to the Type of certification needed.

Core: The Core group *must* be taken, and a passing score received, to obtain *any* of the Types of certification.

Type I: Type I certification pertains to the service of small appliances.

Type II: Type II certification covers high-pressure or very high-pressure system service, except small appliances.

Type III: Type III certification is for the service of low-pressure systems.

Universal: Universal certification consists of Types I, II, and III.

For your convenience, the contents of this book are laid out in the same order as the examination—that is, Core first, then Types I, II, and III respectively. Note that this book presents information and service practices needed to meet EPA requirements for containing, conserving, and reusing refrigerants, thus preventing their escape to the atmosphere. It does *not* teach HVACR system installation, troubleshooting, or repair. RSES has a full library of established Training Courses for that purpose, available through local Chapters and home study. Shorter review courses (Minicourses) also are available from RSES Headquarters. Technician certification is offered through the RSES Educational Foundation in three categories—Refrigeration and Air Conditioning, Heat Pump, and Heating.

In studying the topics of conservation and containment, experienced service technicians will notice that most of the procedures mentioned in this book for maintaining tight systems have been in use for years. These skills must now be applied more diligently than ever.

Students are advised that authorized EPA representatives may require a technician to demonstrate, at his or her place of work, the ability to recover and/or recycle refrigerant. Failure to demonstrate or properly use the equipment may result in revocation of certification.

Section 1

CORE

THE CORE SECTION OF THIS STUDY GUIDE is intended to help refrigeration and air conditioning technicians understand the reasons for handling refrigerants properly.

This section discusses the circumstances that led up to the passing of the Montreal Protocol and subsequent legislation known as EPA Section 608 (this is the section of the law that pertains to HVACR technicians working in the residential and commercial industry).

Because you must successfully complete the Core portion of the EPA examination in order to attain *any* certification, it is recommended that particular attention be paid to this section. *Failure to comply with the regulations contained in this section when working in the refrigeration and air conditioning field may result in large fines and/or imprisonment.*

Many of the concepts and questions included in the Type I (Small Appliances), Type II (High-Pressure), and Type III (Low-Pressure) portions of the EPA exam are taken from the Core section. For this reason, the Core section is the largest section of this book.

Stratospheric ozone

Ozone is a gas, slightly bluish in color and with a pungent odor. Each molecule of ozone is made up of three atoms of oxygen. The oxygen we need to breathe contains only two oxygen atoms in each molecule. Chemically, then, oxygen is O_2 and ozone is O_3. The "ozone layer" consists of ozone in the *stratosphere* (the layer of the earth's atmosphere that extends from an altitude of about 6 miles above the surface to about 25 miles above the surface). The ozone layer is formed by ultraviolet (UV) light from the sun acting on oxygen molecules. It absorbs and scatters the sun's ultraviolet waves, thus preventing harmful amounts of radiation from reaching the earth. For this reason, it is sometimes referred to as the ozone "shield."

Tropospheric ozone

Ozone is also found at times in the lower atmosphere, where we breathe it. In the *troposphere* (the layer of the earth's atmosphere closest to the surface), ozone is caused by ultraviolet radiation from the sun acting on smog and air pollutants on hot summer days. This situation should not be confused with the ozone layer in the stratosphere. Tropospheric or "ground-based" ozone is a harmful pollutant. Stratospheric ozone acts as a protective shield.

Depletion of stratospheric ozone

In June of 1974, Professor Sherwood Rowland and Dr. Mario Molina of the Department of Chemistry at the University of California at Irvine first proposed the theory that certain chlorine-containing compounds could pose a threat to the ozone layer above the earth. The Rowland-Molina theory said that chlorofluorocarbons (CFCs) would ultimately cause damage to the ozone layer, which protects the earth from harmful levels of ultraviolet radiation from the sun.

Since that time, extensive research has confirmed much of the theory, and more is being learned about the way in which ozone is destroyed in the stratosphere. What follows is a summary of our current understanding.

Refrigerants that contain chlorine but not hydrogen (CFCs) are so stable that they do not break down in the lower atmosphere, even 100 years or more after being released. As a result of atmospheric phenomena, such as temperature inversions, tornadoes, etc., these heavier-than-air chemicals rise up to the stratosphere. There the chlorine reacts with ozone, causing it to change back to oxygen and chlorine monoxide. Not all of the chlorine is "used up" in the reaction—each free atom of chlorine goes on to cause more ozone-to-oxygen reactions.

The "ozone hole" is a thinning in the ozone layer over Antarctica. Due to the unique climate in this part of the world, the thinning occurs during the Antarctic spring season (autumn in the Northern Hemisphere). Powerful winds encircle Antarctica during its winter season, isolating the continent from warmer winds that would otherwise migrate from lower latitudes on the earth's surface. In addition, the continent is in darkness during the winter. These two effects combine to produce the coldest temperatures on earth, colder even than the Arctic.

The stratosphere is normally too dry to form clouds, except at the bitterly cold temperatures reached during the Antarctic winter. At these frigid temperatures, clouds of ice and nitric acid called polar stratospheric clouds (PSCs) form in the stratosphere over the Antarctic continent.

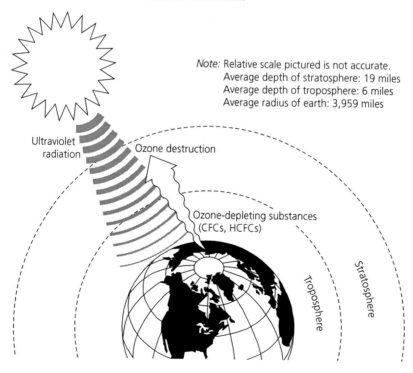

Note: Relative scale pictured is not accurate.
Average depth of stratosphere: 19 miles
Average depth of troposphere: 6 miles
Average radius of earth: 3,959 miles

Ultraviolet radiation

Ozone destruction

Ozone-depleting substances (CFCs, HCFCs)

Troposphere

Stratosphere

Chemical reactions take place on the surfaces of these clouds, converting chlorine from forms that do not react with ozone to other, less stable forms which readily break up in the presence of sunlight and go on to destroy ozone.

Both cold temperatures and sunlight are critical to the ozone depletion process. So it is in the spring, when the sun rises again and while the PSCs are still present, that the thinning of the ozone layer over the Antarctic continent takes place. As the sun warms Antarctica in the spring, the clouds dissipate.

This region is being carefully monitored for the degree to which the ozone thins out, since it has been found to lead to ozone depletion in other parts of the world as well. Significantly reduced ozone levels were detected in 1985, and high chlorine levels were found in 1986. Since that time, ground-based instruments and instrumented aircraft flights through the area have indicated that the ozone depletion problem may be more serious than initially thought.

The illustration on the next page shows how solar radiation breaks down a CFC molecule, which in turn releases chlorine atoms. With chlorine acting as a catalyst, a chain reaction occurs that results in the destruction of ozone (O_3) and the formation of diatomic oxygen (O_2). The chlorine then is available to begin the ozone destruction cycle again. It is now estimated that each free chlorine atom in the stratosphere can destroy as many as 100,000 ozone molecules.

When ozone depletion occurs, more UV radiation penetrates to the earth's surface. Moreover, because of the long atmospheric lifetimes of CFCs, it will take many decades for the ozone layer to return to past concentrations. Bromine-containing compounds, such as those used in halon fire extinguishers, react even more aggressively, destroying ozone (bromine is chemically related to chlorine).

Each CFC refrigerant and halon has been assigned a factor that represents its relative ability to destroy stratospheric ozone. Called the *ozone depletion factor* or, more frequently, *ozone depletion potential* (ODP), this is a number derived from a scale on which

Ozone destruction caused by CFCs

C = carbon atom
Cl = chlorine atom
F = fluorine atom
O = oxygen atom

CFC molecule

1. UV radiation from the sun strikes the CFC molecule and causes a chlorine atom to break away

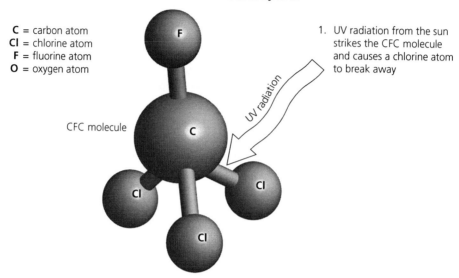

2. The chlorine atom reacts with an ozone molecule to form chlorine monoxide and diatomic oxygen

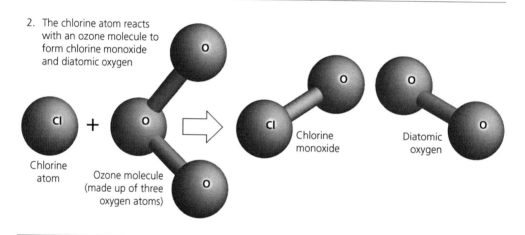

Chlorine atom + Ozone molecule (made up of three oxygen atoms) → Chlorine monoxide + Diatomic oxygen

3. When a free atom of oxygen reacts with a chlorine monoxide molecule, diatomic oxygen is formed and the chlorine atom is released to destroy more ozone

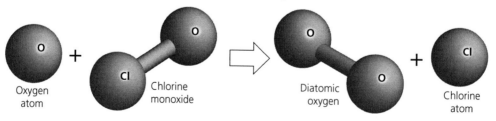

Oxygen atom + Chlorine monoxide → Diatomic oxygen + Chlorine atom

CFC-11 has been assigned a value of 1. Some comparative ODPs are listed below. Note that the bromine-containing halons have factors many times those of the CFC refrigerants.

CFC or halon	ODP
CFC-11.............	1.0
CFC-12.............	1.0
CFC-113............	0.8
CFC-114............	1.0
CFC-115............	0.6
Halon-1211..........	3.0
Halon-1301.........	10.0
Halon-2402..........	6.0

MOLECULAR STRUCTURE AND TERMINOLOGY

Many refrigerants in current use are compounds containing carbon, fluorine, chlorine, and sometimes hydrogen. Notable exceptions are ammonia and HFCs.

CFCs As their name indicates, *chlorofluorocarbons* (CFCs) consist of chlorine, fluorine, and carbon. Because they contain no hydrogen, CFC refrigerants are chemically very stable, even when released into the atmosphere. And because they contain chlorine, they are damaging to the ozone layer—which, high above the earth's surface, shields us from excessive solar radiation.

The combination of these two characteristics gives CFC refrigerants a high ozone depletion potential (ODP), and has made these refrigerants the target of legislation that will reduce their availability and use. Their manufacture was discontinued on January 1, 1996. The following list shows the designation, chemical formula, and molecular structure of the five CFC refrigerants that came under control of the international Montreal Protocol and U.S. EPA regulations as of July 1, 1989:

R-11 — Trichlorofluoromethane — CCl_3F
R-12 — Dichlorodifluoromethane — CCl_2F_2
R-113 — Trichlorotrifluoroethane — CCl_2FCClF_2
R-114 — Dichlorotetrafluoroethane — $CClF_2CClF_2$
R-115 — Chloropentafluoroethane — $CClF_2CF_3$

HCFCs *Hydrochlorofluorocarbons* (HCFCs) make up a second category of refrigerants currently available. Although they contain chlorine, which is damaging to the ozone layer, HCFC refrigerants also contain hydrogen, which makes them chemically less stable once they enter the atmosphere.

HCFC refrigerants decompose when released in the lower atmosphere, and so very little chlorine ever reaches the ozone layer. HCFCs therefore have very low ODPs.

R-22 is an example of an HCFC refrigerant that has been in widespread use for many years. Most residential and small commercial air conditioning equipment uses R-22. R-123 is now being used as a replacement for R-11 in commercial equipment. The chemical formulas and molecular structures of R-22 and R-123 are shown below:

R-22 — Chlorodifluoromethane — $CHClF_2$
R-123 — Dichlorotrifluoroethane — $CHCl_2CF_3$

HFCs *Hydrofluorocarbons* (HFCs) contain no chlorine at all. These refrigerants have an ODP of zero. An example is R-134a, as shown in the diagram below:

R-134a — 1,1,1,2-Tetrafluoroethane — CF_3CH_2F

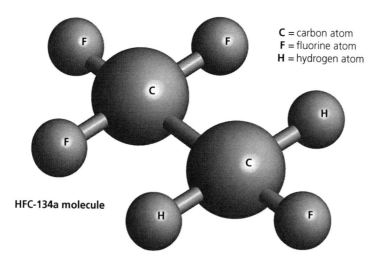

C = carbon atom
F = fluorine atom
H = hydrogen atom

HFC-134a molecule

Because a refrigerant's structure, whether CFC, HCFC, or HFC, has become so important a matter to consider, you often see them referred to with the CFC-, HCFC-, or HFC- prefix, rather than the simple "R-" (which stands for "refrigerant"). For example, R-12 is the same as CFC-12, R-22 is the same as HCFC-22, and R-125 is HFC-125. This is simply a way of pointing out the chemical structure and, therefore, the relative ODP of a refrigerant. Throughout this book, the "R-" prefix will be used interchangeably with the CFC-/HCFC-/HFC- designations.

HEALTH AND ENVIRONMENTAL EFFECTS

Shielding the earth from much of the sun's radiation, the ozone layer is a critical resource safeguarding life on this planet. Should the ozone layer be depleted, more of the sun's damaging rays would penetrate to the earth's surface. Each 1% depletion would increase exposure to damaging UV radiation by 1.5 to 2%. The EPA's assessment of the risks from ozone depletion have focused on the following areas:

▶ Increases in skin cancers

▶ Suppression of the human immune response system

▶ Increases in cataracts

▶ Damage to crops

▶ Damage to aquatic organisms

▶ Increases in ground level ozone

▶ Increased global warming

Human health effects
Skin cancer is already a serious problem in the U.S., but would increase with further depletion of the ozone layer. Under current atmospheric conditions, the greater the distance from the equator, the more effective the ozone layer is as a shield. As a result, there is a natural experiment taking place. People who live farther north are exposed to less damaging UV radiation than

those residing closer to the equator. Not surprisingly, the chances of getting skin cancer follow the same gradient. The closer to the equator, the greater the risk from UV radiation.

Three distinct types of skin cancer would increase if the depletion of the ozone layer were to continue. Basal and squamous cell skin cancers are the two most common types, now affecting about 500,000 people annually in the U.S. If detected early, these cancers are treatable. Even so, approximately 1% of cases result in premature deaths.

Malignant melanoma is far less common but substantially more harmful. About 25,000 cases now occur annually, resulting in 5,000 deaths. While the relationship between exposure to UV radiation and melanoma is a complex one, existing studies provide a basis for estimating future risks associated with ozone depletion.

Cataracts cloud the lens of the eye, thus limiting vision. Although cataracts develop for a variety of reasons, scientific evidence supports the conclusion that increased exposure to UV radiation from ozone depletion would increase the number of people experiencing this eye disorder. Based on studies, if current trends in the use of ozone-depleting gases continued, the number of cataract cases would increase by 1 million (for the population alive today or born before 2075).

Suppression of the immune system is another possible threat to human health resulting from ozone depletion. Research to date suggests that the exposure to UV radiation weakens the ability of the human immune system to fend off certain diseases. Scientists still need to know more about the exact way the immune system is affected, but there is a clear implication that exposure to UV radiation is linked to a wide variety of other diseases.

Plant and marine effects Crops and other terrestrial ecosystems also could be adversely affected by increased exposure to UV radiation. In greenhouse studies, approximately two-thirds of the crops exposed to elevated levels of UV radiation proved sensitive. Field studies of soybeans, for example, have shown that ozone depletion of up to 25% could decrease crop yields by over 20%, with substantially greater reductions in years when climatic stresses were also a factor.

Certain marine organisms, particularly phytoplankton and the larvae of many species, may be sensitive to increased exposure to UV radiation because they spend much of their existence near the surface of the water. Although it is difficult to design experiments duplicating aquatic environments, research to date suggests that adverse effects on productivity and species diversity are related to increased exposure to UV radiation.

Other impacts   Other areas in which scientists are investigating the effects of increased UV radiation include:

- ▶ **Increase in ground-level ozone.** Stratospheric ozone depletion would increase the rate of formation of ground-level (tropospheric) ozone, a major component of what is commonly called smog.

- ▶ **Degradation of polymers.** Ozone depletion would accelerate the weathering (chalking, yellowing, and cracking) of plastics used in outdoor applications.

- ▶ **Changes in climate.** CFCs, HFCs, and HCFCs are also greenhouse gases. This means that they have properties similar to those of carbon dioxide, and thus would contribute to global warming and rising sea levels.

Global nature of the problem   Unlike many other environmental issues, stratospheric ozone protection is truly a global problem. CFCs and halons are used in many countries around the world. Given their long atmospheric lifetimes, they become widely dispersed over time. As a result, the release of these chemicals in one country could adversely affect the stratosphere above other countries—and thereby have an impact on the health and welfare of millions of people.

Many developed nations (and some developing nations) produce CFCs and halons. Most consume the chemicals in a variety of different products. It is estimated that the U.S. consumes over a quarter of the world's CFCs. Other nations are also significant users. In the early 1990s, the approximate consumption of CFCs by country or region could be broken down as follows:

United States. 29%

Other developed nations. 41%

Former USSR and Eastern Europe. 14%

Developing nations. 14%

China/India 2%

Obviously, an international solution is critical if the ozone layer is to be protected from the damage caused by CFCs and halons.

Evidence The enlargement of the ozone hole over Antarctica and accurate measurements reveal that the rise in the amount of chlorine in the stratosphere matches the rise in the amount of fluorine in the stratosphere. Plankton growth in the southern regions of the world has been studied, and the decrease has been documented by biologists' research. The development of cataracts in sheep in Australia and New Zealand and in llamas in Chile verify the health effects. The need for sunscreen with a higher SPF (sun protection factor) number is frequently included in weather reports now in the U.S.

EARLY CONTROLS ON CFCS

During the early 1970s, CFCs used as aerosol propellants constituted over 50% of the total CFC consumption in the U.S. In 1978, following concerns initially raised by the Rowland-Molina theory, the EPA and the Food and Drug Administration (FDA) banned the use of CFCs as aerosol (spray can) propellants in all but a few essential (mostly medical) applications. This significantly reduced the U.S. production and use of CFC-11 and CFC-12.

Unfortunately, very few other countries followed the lead of the U.S. in this ban. Nevertheless, the EPA announced in 1980 that it was considering further restrictions on CFC production for other, non-aerosol uses, due to concern about future growth in the use of CFCs. Two regulatory approaches were proposed at that time: (1) mandatory regulations, and (2) economic incentives, including the sale of required permits.

Because concerns about ozone depletion seemed to be diminishing at the time, the EPA did not immediately pursue regulation within the U.S., but began to focus on developing "international" agreements. However, two new factors brought CFCs back into the arena of public concern in 1986.

One was the connection between CFCs and the theory of global warming (the "greenhouse effect"). The other was new scientific evidence that CFCs aided in the depletion of stratospheric ozone, and that a "hole" had developed in the ozone layer over Antarctica.

THE MONTREAL PROTOCOL

On September 16, 1987, in Montreal, Canada, 24 nations and the European Economic Community (EEC) signed the Montreal Protocol. The treaty established trade provisions and phase-out schedules for ozone-depleting substances. Recognizing the global nature of the problem, most of the nations that were recognized as major producers and consumers of CFCs and halons signed the agreement. Other nations, including the former Soviet Union, indicated that, following further consultations, there was a possibility of their becoming signatories.

In 1990, at a meeting in London, the U.S. and 55 other nations signed an agreement that updated and strengthened the provisions of the original Protocol. The schedule for phasing out CFCs was moved up, and a declaration of intent to phase out HCFCs was added. Further revisions were made at a meeting in Copenhagen in 1992. More than 90 nations attended the Copenhagen meeting, illustrating the growing concern among members of the international community about the ozone depletion issue.

U.S. CLEAN AIR ACT AMENDMENTS

President Bush signed the 1990 Amendments to the Clean Air Act on November 15, 1990. The amendments establish a National Recycling and Emissions Reduction Program to regulate the use and disposal of substances (including CFCs and HCFCs) that are harmful to humans and the environment.

Title VI is entitled *Stratospheric Ozone Protection*. Title VII is entitled *Provisions Relating to Enforcement*. Section 608 of Title VI contains the National Recycling and Emission Reduction Program. The objectives of this program are to reduce the use and emissions of ozone-depleting substances to the lowest achievable level, and to maximize the recapture and recycling of such substances. The amendments set new standards for the safe disposal of ozone-depleting substances and establish federally mandated certification procedures for those engaged in servicing air conditioners.

To accomplish some of these goals, the regulations require that new refrigeration and air conditioning appliances be equipped with a servicing aperture or similar device to facilitate the recapture of refrigerants during service and repair of the appliance. The regulations also affect service technicians who repair or service such appliances.

Under the regulations, an HVACR service technician may not "knowingly vent or otherwise knowingly release or dispose of any substance used as a refrigerant in such appliance in a manner which permits such substance to enter the environment. De minimis releases associated with good faith attempts to recapture and recycle or safely dispose of any such substance shall not be subject to prohibition set forth in the preceding sentence."

The above prohibition applies regardless of whether the release was intentional. A service technician who even "inadvertently" releases a refrigerant into the atmosphere is violating the law. Releases are considered *de minimis* (minimal) only if the required practices are followed, and if certified recovery or recycling equipment is used.

The penalties and fines for violating the above provisions can be severe. The EPA is authorized to seek various levels of legal redress against any person who violates the stated prohibitions. The agency may obtain an injunction against the offending party, prohibiting the individual from discharging refrigerants into the air. In more serious cases, a penalty of up to $27,500 *per day* may be imposed on the offender with the approval of the U.S. District Court. In addition, the agency may seek to have criminal penalties and prison terms (not exceeding 5 years) brought against any person who knowingly releases refrigerants into the atmosphere. Criminal fines and imprisonment also may be assessed against any person who makes any false material statement or representation in any report, notice, or application required by the EPA.

Furthermore, any person who negligently or knowingly releases into the ambient air any hazardous air pollutant, and who as a result of the release places another person in imminent danger of death or serious bodily injury, may be subject to criminal fines and penalties. In the case of an intentional discharge, the prison term may be a maximum of 15 years.

Finally, in order to encourage others to report violations of the Act, the EPA is authorized to pay rewards of up to $10,000 to any person who furnishes information that leads to a criminal conviction of another person for violation of the above prohibitions.

All HVACR service personnel should undertake to be fully trained in all currently recommended service and repair procedures and techniques applicable to appliances containing refrigerants. In addition, service providers should institute procedures to ensure that they do not permit even an inadvertent discharge of refrigerants into the atmosphere.

Disposal, as described in the pages of the Clean Air Act, means that used refrigerant must be disposed of according to EPA requirements. Some large facilities may have reclaim equipment available, but the majority of service locations will not be able to meet the ARI 700 standards for reclaimed refrigerant. Most service technicians have little choice but to send recovered refrigerant to a reclaim facility for proper handling.

Phase-out schedule The phase-out of various ozone-depleting compounds was amended from its original schedule in 1993. Some countries would like to accelerate the phase-out of HCFCs still more. As of the publication of this book, the phase-out schedule stands as follows:

▶ **Halons.** Production and import of halons was discontinued as of the end of 1993.

▶ **CFCs.** CFC production and import, except for "essential uses," was discontinued as of January 1, 1996. (Some production and import of certain CFCs may be allowed if their use is determined by the parties to the Montreal Protocol to be "essential.")

▶ **HCFCs.** HCFC-141b will be phased out as of the year 2003. Production and import of HCFC-22 and HCFC-142b for new equipment will be discontinued in 2010, and these refrigerants will no longer be manufactured or imported as of 2020. Production and import of other HCFCs (including HCFC-123) for new equipment will cease in 2020, with total phase-out in 2030. Some production and import of certain HCFCs may be allowed after applicable phase-out dates, if their use is determined by the parties to the Protocol to be "essential."

Prohibition on venting

The Clean Air Act prohibited venting of CFC and HCFC refrigerants as of July 1992. An amendment by the EPA, effective in November 1995, included the *substitutes* for these refrigerants as well. Thus, all currently used compounds (including HFCs) *must* be recovered.

Section 608 of the Clean Air Act prohibits individuals from knowingly venting ozone-depleting compounds used as refrigerants into the atmosphere while maintaining, servicing, repairing, or disposing of air conditioning or refrigeration equipment. Only four types of releases are permitted by law:

1. "De minimis" quantities of refrigerant released in the course of making good faith attempts to recapture and recycle or safely dispose of refrigerant.

2. Refrigerants emitted in the course of normal operation of air conditioning and refrigeration equipment (as opposed to during maintenance, service, etc.), such as from mechanical purging and leaks. However, the EPA requires the repair of substantial leaks, as explained in the regulations.

3. Mixtures of nitrogen and R-22 that are used as holding charges, or as leak test gases. In these cases, the ozone-depleting compound is not used as a refrigerant. However, a technician may not avoid recovering refrigerant by adding nitrogen to a charged system. Before nitrogen is added, the system must be evacuated to the appropriate level, as stated in Table 1 of the EPA regulations (see page 43). Otherwise, the CFC or HCFC vented along with the nitrogen will be considered a refrigerant. Similarly, pure CFCs or HCFCs released from equipment will be presumed to be refrigerants, and their release will be considered a violation of the prohibition on venting.

4. Small releases of refrigerant that result from purging hoses, or from connecting or disconnecting hoses to charge or service equipment will not be considered violations of the prohibition on venting. However, recovery and recycling equipment manufactured after November 15, 1993 must be equipped with low-loss fittings (see "Low-Loss Fitting" in the *Selected Definitions* section of the EPA regulations).

EPA regulations The EPA has established various regulations that should be studied and followed by any individual involved with the possible release of the refrigerants as defined by these rules. A summary of the EPA regulations implementing Section 608 of the Clean Air Act is available from RSES. Ask for publication 630-110.

REPLACEMENT REFRIGERANTS AND OILS

Due to concerns about the depletion of the earth's protective stratospheric ozone layer, CFC refrigerants were phased out of production by the year 1996. HCFC refrigerants are being phased out in stages and will no longer be produced by the year 2030. Azeotropes such as R-500, R-502, and R-503 gradually will become unavailable, since their constituent components also were phased out in 1996.

Replacement refrigerants have been developed, tested, and are now in use. Additional research is proceeding at a rapid pace in search of more compatible replacements. Key considerations for any new refrigerant include: chemical stability in the system, compatibility, toxicity, flammability, thermal characteristics, efficiency, ease of detection when searching for leaks, environmental effects, compatibility with lubricants in hermetic systems, and cost, to name a few.

In general, R-123 is intended to replace R-11, and R-134a has replaced R-12 in many OEM (original equipment manufacturer) applications. Some of the other replacements already in use are "near-azeotropic" blends. Some terminology is in order at this point.

Service technicians are familiar with *azeotropic* refrigerants, such as R-500 and R-502. An azeotrope is a two-part ("binary") mixture that performs as one refrigerant with a specific boiling temperature at a given pressure. *Zeotropes* are mixtures that exhibit "temperature glide"—that is, at a given pressure, the blend evaporates and condenses over a *range* of temperatures.

The *near-azeotropic* blends are zeotropes with a temperature glide of less than 5°C. Those currently available are mostly three-part ("ternary") mixtures. You may hear these referred to as "zeotropes," "near-azeotropes," "ternary blends," or simply "blends." They have a great many advantages, if used correctly.

Note that, from a technical standpoint, azeotropes, near-azeotropes, and zeotropes could be either binary or ternary mixtures, or they could be mixtures of several refrigerants. Currently, however, azeotropes are binary and most near-azeotropes are ternary. This could change in the future. Azeotropes are assigned "R" numbers in the -500 series. Near-azeotropes and zeotropes are designated by -400 series numbers.

Due to the different vapor pressures of refrigerants in the mixture, *near-azeotropes and zeotropes should not be charged into a system in the vapor state. They should always be liquid-charged.* The difference in vapor pressures could result in the most volatile refrigerant of the mixture leaving the cylinder at a faster rate than that of the others, when the refrigerant is in a two-phase condition. This separation is called *fractionation*.

Heavy reliance will be placed on continued use of HCFCs (such as R-22 and R-123) until they are no longer available. Residential air conditioning, non-industrial heat pumps, and positive-displacement chillers will continue to operate on R-22 for some years to come. Current candidates for use as an OEM replacement for R-22 are R-407 and R-410A. Equipment utilizing R-407C and R-410A is now on the market.

Many existing system retrofits will require the replacement of existing hardware (CFC-12 to HCFC-22 retrofits, for example). The existing refrigerant cannot simply be removed from the system and replaced with another. Lubricant replacement also may be necessary.

The process of producing replacement refrigerants has not been an easy one. The EPA has issued a list of approved replacement refrigerants called the SNAP (Significant New Alternative Policy) list. This list should be used to aid in the selection of a replacement refrigerant.

To shorten the time needed for testing the toxicity of new refrigerants, fourteen refrigerant manufacturers formed the Program for Alternative Fluorocarbon Toxicity Testing (PAFTT). The most widely recognized industry standard for flammability and toxicity levels currently is ASHRAE Standard 34.

Preliminary results of testing R-123 showed some concerns for toxicity. Various refrigerant and equipment manufacturers responded to this news in various ways. Some stopped product shipments, others lowered their recommended exposure levels. The original allowable exposure limit for R-123 was 30 parts per million (ppm) for an 8 to 12-hour workday. This number has since been increased to 50 ppm, after additional testing was performed. Some equipment manufacturers feel that R-123 can still be used safely in chillers as long as ASHRAE Standard 15, *Safety Code for Mechanical Refrigeration*, is followed. Key elements of this standard are:

▶ The use of a refrigerant-specific detector for all regulated refrigerants. The sensor sounds an alarm and starts mechanical ventilation.

▶ The use of mechanical ventilation in the equipment room, sized according to ASHRAE Standard 15.

▶ The availability of at least one approved self-contained breathing apparatus kept in a location convenient to the equipment room, for emergency purposes.

▶ Piping that directs any release from ruptured disks or purges to the outdoors.

In case of a spill of *any* refrigerant, the area should be evacuated and ventilated.

Regarding performance in centrifugal chillers, R-123 provides a capacity decrease of 0 to 15%, with a kW/ton increase of 6 to 8%. Gear and/or motor changes may be needed with R-123, along with the possibility of cooler tube changes.

The properties of R-134a are very similar to those of R-12, and it is believed that, with proper equipment redesign, efficiencies will be similar. In chillers, with a gear change or tube change, original capacity can usually be met, with a kW/ton increase of 1 to 2%.

Refrigerant oils *Mineral oils* have long been used with CFC and HCFC refrigerants. However, there are *miscibility* (the ability to mix) problems with mineral oil and the new refrigerant blends, as well as with some of the single-component replacement refrigerants.

Polyolester oils (POEs, also called "polyols" or "esters") work well with almost any of the commonly available blends or single-component refrigerants. POEs are *required* when using HFC refrigerants or HFC blends. But POEs are very expensive. *Alkylbenzene* (AB) oil is the lubricant of choice for the HCFC blends, because of its lower cost.

In addition to their significantly higher cost, POE oils do not mix with other lubricants—which means that when a system is retrofitted with a replacement refrigerant or blend, multiple flushes are required to reduce any remaining mineral oil to an extremely low level. This makes the retrofit of HFC-134a into existing CFC-12 systems both time-consuming and costly. Compressor manufacturers specify the maximum concentration of mineral oil acceptable in a polyolester for use with their systems (generally 5%). Any mineral oil remaining in the system will remain in the evaporator and decrease heat transfer. It should also be noted that different compressor manufacturers are approving different brands of the new lubricants.

Two additional cautionary notes concerning POEs: First, they are very *hygroscopic*—that is, they absorb moisture very readily. Be especially cautious when handling this type of oil to minimize its exposure to the air or any other source of moisture or high humidity. Second, avoid the use of carbon dioxide (CO_2) in conjunction with POE lubricants. The POE lubricant dissolves the CO_2, making it almost impossible to remove.

AB oil is much more tolerant of mineral oil in a system—a single oil change may be satisfactory to reduce the remaining mineral oil to less than the 20% usually required.

There are exceptions to the guidelines given here. When changing system refrigerant, always consult the original equipment manufacturer for specific recommendations.

REFRIGERATION CYCLE

The basic refrigeration system

The diagram on the next page illustrates a basic vapor compression refrigeration or air conditioning system. The main components shown (compressor, condenser, receiver, metering device, evaporator, and accumulator) are what make the system work, and are sufficient to illustrate the operation.

The *compressor* draws cool refrigerant vapor from the evaporator and compresses it. This increases both the temperature and pressure of the refrigerant.

The hot, high-pressure refrigerant vapor flows through the *condenser*, where it is cooled sufficiently to change to a high-pressure liquid. Cooling of the condenser is usually accomplished by drawing outdoor air through the coil, but water-cooled and evaporative condensers also are used.

The warm, high-pressure liquid passes from the condenser to the *receiver*. When a receiver is used in a system, it serves several purposes. It functions as a type of surge tank, storing excess liquid refrigerant. The amount of refrigerant in a liquid state will vary proportionally with the system load. The receiver, if properly sized, may hold the entire refrigerant charge. This can decrease recovery time and speed up service procedures.

From the receiver, the warm, high-pressure liquid refrigerant flows through the "liquid line" to the *metering device*. The metering device, also called a *flow control device*, generally is

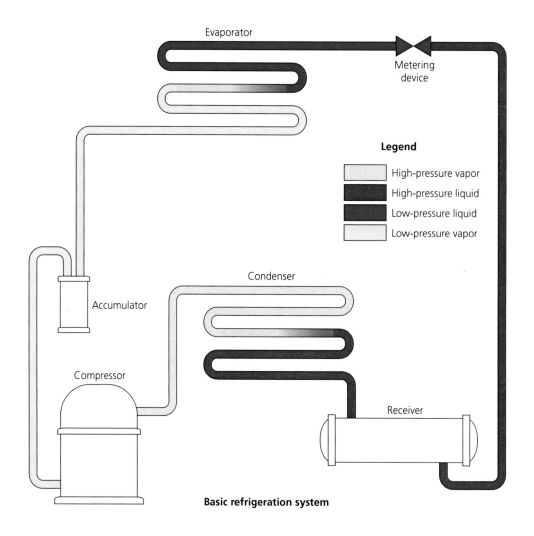

Basic refrigeration system

a capillary tube, a fixed orifice, or a thermostatic expansion valve, but it may also be a hand expansion valve or a float control. In any case, its purpose is the same—to control the flow of liquid refrigerant and reduce its pressure.

Warm, low-pressure liquid refrigerant leaves the metering device and enters the *evaporator*, where it boils into a vapor due to the reduced pressure created by the suction side of the compressor. As the refrigerant vaporizes, it absorbs heat from its surroundings. This is where the cooling effect occurs. In a comfort cooling system, a blower circulates air over the cold evaporator and delivers it to the conditioned space.

From the evaporator, the cool, low-pressure refrigerant vapor travels through the "suction line" into the *accumulator*, if one is used (or, if there is no accumulator, directly to the compressor). A suction accumulator is employed for one purpose—to protect the compressor from liquid refrigerant. Accumulators frequently are used with freezer applications and heat pumps, and in comfort cooling systems when line lengths are excessive.

The compressor discharge line, the condenser, the receiver, and the liquid line to the metering device all contain high-pressure refrigerant and are referred to as the "high side" of the system. The outlet of the metering device, the evaporator, the suction accumulator, and all of the piping to the suction side of the compressor contain low-pressure refrigerant, and thus make up the "low side."

Refrigerants Various refrigerants are best suited to particular applications. Small appliances such as refrigerators and water coolers once used R-12, which has been replaced for the most part by R-134a. Comfort cooling systems, both split and unitary, operate on R-22. Due to the upcoming phase-out of HCFCs, systems are starting to appear with R-410A and other refrigerant blends. R-502, which was used extensively in medium-temperature and low-temperature applications for many years, has been replaced by a variety of different blends.

While the refrigerant used in a system generally is indicated on the unit's nameplate, it is a good idea to verify the refrigerant being used, especially since there are so many blends on the market today. Several types of field-grade refrigerant analyzers are available. If you encounter a mixture of new and retrofitted equipment on a frequent basis, such an analyzer may be a wise investment.

When refrigerant information is not available, service gauges, a thermometer, and a refrigerant temperature-pressure chart can be used to determine the refrigerant in the system. Remember that before you begin refrigerant recovery, you *must* be absolutely certain of the refrigerant that you are recovering, or you may inadvertently mix refrigerants in the recovery tank. Mixed refrigerants in most cases must be destroyed.

Service gauges   A typical gauge manifold consists of a low-pressure (compound) gauge used on the low side of the system, and a high-pressure gauge for the system's high side. The compound gauge is often blue in color. It measures pressures in pounds per square inch gauge (psig) and vacuum in inches of mercury (in. Hg). The high-pressure gauge is usually red, and reads pressures from 0 to 500 psi. When the valves of the manifold are positioned properly, the low-pressure gauge, connected by its hose to the low side of the system, will read pressure or vacuum. The high-pressure gauge, connected by its hose to the high side of the system, will read pressure. The center hose is used for refrigerant recovery, evacuation, and charging. *Note:* Be aware that R-410A systems operate at significantly higher pressures than R-22 systems, and require the use of different gauge manifolds and hoses.

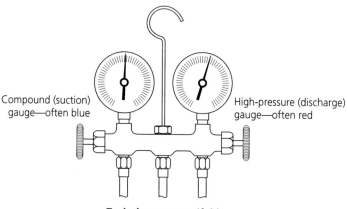

Compound (suction) gauge—often blue

High-pressure (discharge) gauge—often red

Typical gauge manifold

Refrigerant temperature-pressure charts

In the absence of air or any other noncondensables, the vapor pressure of a single-component refrigerant at saturation (vapor in contact with its liquid) will correspond accurately with the temperature listed on a reliable temperature-pressure (T-P) chart (a typical T-P chart is shown on the following page). For example, the evaporating temperature of R-22 at 0 psig is about −40°F. The pressure of R-22 in a non-operating system at 80°F is 143.7 psig. R-22 at a temperature of 35°F (3°F above the freezing point of water) has a pressure of 61.5 psig.

When you take temperature or gauge readings for purposes of comparing them to a T-P chart, remember that the temperature must be stable in order to be known accurately. When you take a reading on a refrigerant cylinder, for example, the best way to be sure that you get accurate results is to let the cylinder stabilize at ambient temperature. This is also the first step in determining if a cylinder of refrigerant contains noncondensables. If the pressure in a cylinder of a known refrigerant reads higher or lower than the pressure indicated on the T-P chart for the cylinder's temperature, the refrigerant may be mixed, or contaminated by noncondensables. Conversely, assuming that the refrigerant is not mixed or contaminated, it may be identified by finding the refrigerant on the chart that corresponds to your temperature and pressure readings. At most normal temperatures, most refrigerants have sufficiently different temperature-pressure relationships to identify them in this way.

Service procedures

Noncondensables are not the only contaminants that can cause problems in refrigeration systems. Moisture can cause a freeze-up in the metering device, and can contribute to the formation of hydrochloric and hydrofluoric acids in the system. Proper evacuation of the system prior to recharging will remove both air and water that may be present, and is also a good method of leak testing. Caution must be taken to ensure that a hermetically sealed compressor is not started when the system is in a deep vacuum, since this could cause an electrical failure in the compressor motor. An acid test of the refrigerant oil should be performed any time the system has a leak or failure of one of the major components. A positive reading will dictate the installation of filter-driers in both the liquid and suction lines. Cleaning the system by flushing with refrigerant is no longer an option.

Temp (°F)	R-123	R-11	R-134a	R-12	R-500	R-22	R-502	R-410A
-150				* 29.6	* 29.5	* 29.4	* 29.1	
-140			* 29.6	* 29.4	* 29.2	* 29.1	* 28.5	
-130			* 29.4	* 29.1	* 28.8	* 28.5	* 27.8	
-120			* 29.1	* 28.6	* 28.3	* 27.7	* 26.7	
-110			* 28.7	* 27.9	* 27.5	* 26.6	* 25.3	
-100		* 29.7	* 28.0	* 27.0	* 26.9	* 25.1	* 23.3	
-90		* 29.6	* 27.1	* 25.8	* 24.9	* 23.0	* 20.6	
-80	* 29.7	* 29.5	* 25.7	* 24.1	* 22.9	* 20.2	* 17.2	
-70	* 29.6	* 29.4	* 24.0	* 21.9	* 20.3	* 16.6	* 12.7	* 7.0
-60	* 29.4	* 29.1	* 21.6	* 19.0	* 17.0	* 11.9	* 7.2	* 0.3
-50	* 29.2	* 28.8	* 18.6	* 15.4	* 12.8	* 6.1	* 0.2	5.0
-40	* 28.8	* 28.3	* 14.7	* 11.0	* 7.6	0.6	4.1	10.8
-35	* 28.6	* 28.0	* 12.3	* 8.4	* 4.6	2.6	6.5	14.0
-30	* 28.3	* 27.7	* 9.7	* 5.5	* 1.2	4.9	9.2	17.8
-25	* 28.1	* 27.4	* 6.8	* 2.3	1.2	7.5	12.1	21.9
-20	* 27.7	* 26.9	* 3.6	0.6	3.2	10.2	15.3	26.3
-15	* 27.3	* 26.5	0.0	2.5	5.4	13.2	18.8	31.1
-10	* 26.9	* 25.9	2.0	4.5	7.8	16.5	22.6	36.4
-5	* 26.4	* 25.3	4.1	6.7	10.4	20.1	26.7	42.6
0	* 25.8	* 24.6	6.5	9.2	13.3	24.0	31.1	48.2
5	* 25.2	* 23.9	9.1	11.8	16.4	28.3	35.9	54.9
10	* 24.5	* 23.0	12.0	14.7	19.7	32.8	41.0	62.1
15	* 23.7	* 22.1	15.1	17.7	23.3	37.8	46.5	69.9
20	* 22.8	* 21.0	18.4	21.1	27.2	43.1	52.5	78.2
25	* 21.8	* 19.8	22.1	24.6	31.4	48.8	58.8	87.2
30	* 20.7	* 18.5	26.1	28.5	36.0	54.9	65.6	96.8
35	* 19.5	* 17.1	30.4	32.6	40.8	61.5	72.8	107.0
40	* 18.1	* 15.5	35.0	37.0	46.0	68.5	80.5	118.0
45	* 16.6	* 13.8	40.0	41.7	51.6	76.1	88.7	129.5
50	* 15.0	* 12.0	45.4	46.7	57.5	84.1	97.4	142.0
55	* 13.1	* 9.9	51.2	52.1	63.8	92.6	106.6	156.0
60	* 11.2	* 7.7	57.4	57.8	70.6	101.6	116.4	170.0
65	* 9.0	* 5.3	64.0	63.8	77.7	111.3	126.7	185.0
70	* 6.6	* 2.7	71.1	70.2	85.3	121.4	137.6	200.0
75	* 4.1	0.1	78.6	77.0	93.4	132.2	149.1	217.0
80	* 1.3	1.6	86.7	84.2	101.9	143.7	161.2	235.0
85	0.9	3.2	95.2	91.7	110.9	155.7	174.0	254.0
90	2.5	4.9	104.3	99.7	120.5	168.4	187.4	274.0
95	4.2	6.8	113.9	108.2	130.5	181.8	201.4	295.0
100	6.1	8.8	124.1	117.0	141.1	196.0	216.2	317.0
105	8.1	10.9	134.9	126.4	152.2	210.8	231.7	340.0
110	10.2	13.2	146.3	136.2	163.9	226.4	247.9	364.0
115	12.6	15.7	158.4	146.5	176.3	242.8	264.9	390.0
120	15.0	18.3	171.1	157.3	189.2	260.0	282.7	417.0
125	17.7	21.1	184.5	168.6	202.7	278.1	301.3	445.0
130	20.5	24.0	198.7	180.5	216.9	297.0	320.6	475.0
135	23.5	27.1	213.5	192.9	231.8	316.7	341.2	506.0
140	26.7	30.5	229.2	205.9	247.4	337.4	362.6	538.0
145	30.2	34.0	245.6	219.5	263.7	359.1	384.9	573.0
150	33.8	37.7	262.8	233.7	280.7	381.7	408.4	608.0

Pressures are shown as psig, except (*) indicates inches of mercury vacuum.

Temperature-pressure chart

Preventing leaks is now more important than ever before. When servicing small appliances, always check access valves that may be field-installed for leaks. Due to the tendency of these valves to leak over time, it is a good practice to remove the solderless type of access fittings properly when service is complete.

"THE THREE Rs"

Definitions

In the past, the terms *recover, recycle,* and *reclaim* were used almost interchangeably. However, as the industry realized that more specific terminology was needed to distinguish among these three distinctly different procedures, specific definitions have been developed.

The following definitions appear in ASHRAE Guideline 3-1990 and are appearing in other standards and guidelines within the industry. It is important to understand the differences among these definitions, and to use the proper terms.

▶ **Recover.** To remove refrigerant in any condition from a system and store it in an external container without necessarily testing or processing it in any way.

▶ **Recycle.** To clean refrigerant for reuse by oil separation and single or multiple passes through devices, such as replaceable-core filter-driers, which reduce moisture, acidity, and particulate matter. The term "recycle" usually applies to procedures implemented at the field job site or at a local service shop.

▶ **Reclaim.** To reprocess refrigerant to new product specifications. The means used may include distillation. Chemical analysis of the refrigerant is required to determine that appropriate product specifications are met. The term "reclaim" usually implies the use of processes or procedures available only at a reprocessing or manufacturing facility.

Notes regarding reclaim

Chemical analysis is the key requirement in the definition of *reclaim.* The phrase "new product specifications" currently means ARI Standard 700, and chemical analysis is needed to ensure that the standard is met. Regardless of the purity levels reached by a reprocessing method, the refrigerant is not *reclaimed* unless it has been chemically analyzed and meets the standard.

Because the purity standard is the determining factor, some industry experts consider recycled refrigerant to be reclaimed if the refrigerant is chemically analyzed and qualifies for purity under ARI Standard 700.

OPTIONS

Recover and destroy

In some instances, a refrigerant is so badly contaminated or mixed with other refrigerants that effective reclaiming is impossible. Once CFCs are contaminated or mixed, they can never be used again. The only option is to destroy the refrigerants, and the only method is incineration, which is an expensive undertaking. CFCs are difficult to destroy not only because of their inherent stability, but also because fluorine is released during the incineration process. The process must be able to contain the released fluorine. Always send refrigerant to an authorized treatment facility for destruction. Even waste oils containing high amounts of refrigerant can be harmful and destructive.

Recover and reuse without processing

In some cases, the refrigerant in the system may still be in good condition. It can be removed while repair or maintenance is performed on the system, and then transferred back into the unit. You must handle the removal and transfer of the refrigerant in a proper manner in order to avoid contaminating it. Many service personnel routinely test the refrigerant and keep a record of the results. This allows them to track the condition of the refrigerant and the system over its operating life. It also helps to identify possible problems before they occur. This avoids unplanned downtime and prevents expensive repairs.

Transfer of the refrigerant into a storage container must be done properly. The transfer equipment must be designed for the specific type of refrigerant. The storage container must be clean and properly designed to contain the refrigerant.

Recover and recycle on-site

When operation of a system indicates that the refrigerant is deficient, the refrigerant may need to be processed to remove various contaminants. This works best in small operating appliances, where the amount of refrigerant and the operating standards of the equipment allow on-site recycling of the refrigerant. Recently, standards and modes for this process have been established for mobile air conditioning systems.

REFRIGERANT RECOVERY METHODS

Recovering refrigerant is the first step in preventive maintenance or repair of equipment. Simply put, recovery means transferring the system's refrigerant into a refillable refrigerant cylinder. If the refrigerant was not contaminated by a hermetic motor burnout or other cause, it may be of adequate quality to be charged back into the system after repairs are completed. Or, the recovered refrigerant may require further processing before it can be returned to the system. This may mean on-site recycling or off-site reclaiming.

Remember that recovery and recycling equipment manufactured on or after November 15, 1993 must be tested by an EPA-approved testing organization to ensure that it meets EPA requirements. Equipment that was manufactured before November 15, 1993 does not need to be certified by an EPA-approved testing organization, even if it was purchased after that date. When you buy equipment, be sure to check the date of manufacture. Also check that equipment manufactured before the 1993 date can achieve the required vacuums as listed in Table 1 of the EPA regulations (see page 43).

Recovery and recovery/recycling equipment comes in a variety of designs:

▶ One type removes liquid only.

▶ A second type removes refrigerant in vapor form only.

▶ A third type removes both liquid and vapor, but does not separate the system oil from the refrigerant. (It goes into the storage cylinder exactly as it was in the system.)

▶ A fourth type removes liquid and vapor, *and* separates system oil.

Each of these has advantages and disadvantages. The liquid-only recovery is fast, but it leaves vapor in the system. The vapor-only unit removes all of the refrigerant, but is considerably slower. Recovery machines that separate the refrigeration or air conditioning system's oil from the refrigerant are not necessarily better than those that do not. The primary difference is the disposition of the oil. Reclaimers charge for the disposal of the used oil, and some states and municipalities have regulations that the user must follow.

The process of recovering refrigerant is similar regardless of the equipment used. The best place to start is with proper equipment. Manifolds should be in good condition with no leaks. Hoses that are non-permeable are preferred. At the very least, they should have tight fittings.

Some recovery units require evacuation before each use. Many need to be evacuated when a different refrigerant is being recovered—for example, when you are repairing an R-12 system after an R-22 system. If only a storage cylinder is used, it must be evacuated to at least 1,000 microns.

Once the initial set-up has been completed, recovery can begin. Generally, the procedure follows these basic guidelines: A hose is connected from a service valve on the system being repaired to the inlet of the recovery system. The hose should be as short as possible to reduce pressure drop, refrigerant emissions, and recovery time. The location of the service valve depends on the type of machine. Once the refrigerant has traveled through the machine, it is transferred into the refillable storage cylinder. If the recovery unit does not separate the oil, the refrigerant is ready to send on to a reclaiming station. If the oil is separated, drain and handle it according to local legislation.

Caution: Never mix refrigerants in a recovery vessel. This may render the refrigerant impossible to reclaim.

Procedures   Empty recovery cylinders must be completely evacuated before being filled. This avoids contamination of the recovered refrigerant by air, moisture, or remaining traces of other refrigerants. Evacuate to a minimum of 1,000 microns.

For a faster and more efficient recovery, chill the refillable cylinder and keep it cool during the procedure. This can be done by setting the cylinder in a bucket of ice. There are also dry chemicals on the market that can be mixed with water to create low temperatures. The mixture is then poured into the bucket in which the cylinder is immersed during the transfer process. The lower temperature of the cylinder reduces the pressure of the refrigerant inside it. Conversely, if the system from which you are removing refrigerant is at a low ambient temperature, the recovery process will be slower.

Before beginning recovery, check the positions of all service valves and the oil level of the recovery unit. Recover the refrigerant into the system's own receiver or storage tank if it has one. It is most efficient to recover liquid first (from the system's liquid line), then vapor. Recovering refrigerant in vapor phase will leave the oil in the system, minimizing oil loss.

When recovering from small appliances, first identify the refrigerant that you are about to recover. Older refrigerators,

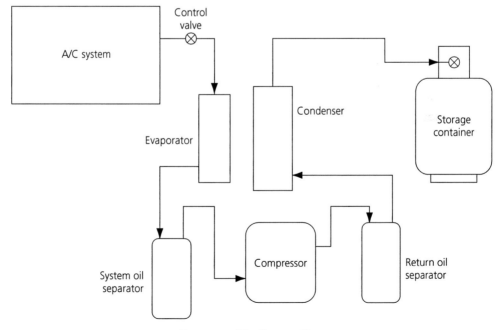

Recovery with oil separation

particularly those built before 1950, may contain non-fluorocarbon refrigerants, which must *not* be recovered with current recovery equipment. The same is true of many recreational vehicle appliances, both old and new. When access fittings need to be installed, they should be checked for leaks. Follow these guidelines when using system-dependent (passive) recovery equipment:

▶ If the appliance compressor does not run, warm the compressor oil and tap the compressor. This will help release refrigerant trapped in the oil.

▶ If the appliance compressor does not run, recover refrigerant from both the high and low sides of the system for a complete recovery. This will also speed the recovery process.

▶ If the appliance compressor is operable, run it and recover the refrigerant from the high side.

When recovering refrigerant from chillers, maintain water circulation in order to prevent freezing.

Slight amounts of refrigerant may escape during these procedures, but U.S. Federal regulations state that "*de minimis* (minimal) releases associated with good faith attempts to recapture and recycle or safely dispose of any such substance (refrigerant) shall not be subject to the prohibition" (against venting).

Safety   The following safety rules must be followed when you use any recovery equipment:

▶ Use only cylinders certified by the Department of Transportation (DOT) as being refillable. All cylinders must be recertified every five years.

▶ Use only fully evacuated and clean cylinders.

▶ *Never* fill a cylinder over 80%. If there is any chance that the cylinder will be exposed to temperatures over 130°F, fill only to 60%. This allows for expansion of the refrigerant when the cylinder warms up. Failure to leave adequate expansion space can cause the cylinder to explode, resulting in severe injury or death. Depending on the recovery equipment and cylinders used, there are several ways to determine the 80% fill level. You can calculate it by weight, using an accurate scale. You also may use a mechanical float device in the cylinder, or an electronic shutoff device.

▶ Be careful not to trap liquid refrigerant between service valves.

▶ *Never* mix different refrigerants.

▶ Plainly mark the type of refrigerant in refillable cylinders. Use each cylinder only for the type of refrigerant for which it is marked.

▶ Restore a contaminated refrigerant to useful purity by recycling or reclaiming, or destroy it properly.

▶ Handle cylinders with care. Do not drop or bump. Keep cylinders in a vertical position. Secure them to prevent them from tipping over. *Never* heat a cylinder with a torch or open flame.

LEAK DETECTION

System pressurization

Checking for leaks while a system is pressurized is preferred, since it makes the leaks easier to detect. In low-pressure systems, or in any system that has lost substantial charge, it may be necessary to raise the system pressure before leak testing. This is almost always required when the leak is thought to be on the low side of a low-pressure system. Because such a system operates at a pressure below atmospheric, leaks are inward, not outward from the system.

The preferred method of raising low-side pressure is by carefully raising the temperature—for example, by using controlled-temperature warm water. Several chiller manufacturers offer packaged hot-water generators. Warm tap water also may be used, if available. The first step in warm-water pressurization is to valve off the condenser and evaporator water circuits. The next step is to circulate the warm water into the evaporator bundle. This causes the refrigerant pressure to rise.

Avoid damage due to thermal shock by raising the temperature slowly. Be careful not to raise the low-side pressure *too* high. The rupture disks in a low-pressure system will open at 15 psig, so never raise the pressure beyond approximately 10 psig.

Low-pressure system pressure also may be raised by using heat blankets, such as used in the PREVAC system.

Another procedure that can be used to raise any system's pressure is to mix dry nitrogen with a small quantity of refrigerant (HCFCs only). Always use a pressure regulator on the nitrogen cylinder. A pressure relief valve downstream from the regulator is also recommended. It is best if the two gases are mixed first, and then added to the system together. Otherwise, the second gas added will push the first gas farther back into the system, and the system must sit idle until the gases have mixed. In such cases, there is a method to test whether the gases have mixed: Bleed a small amount from a system point farthest from where the nitrogen and refrigerant were added, and use a leak detector to find if the trace refrigerant is present.

Remember that any refrigerant remaining in the system must first be recovered to the evacuation level listed in Table 1 of the EPA regulations (shown on the next page) before a mixture of nitrogen and trace refrigerant is added. (*Note:* HFC-134a *must* be removed before pressurizing with nitrogen. The nitrogen and HFC-134a mix will create a new partial azeotrope. The resulting combination must be removed and destroyed.) Before using any method of pressurization on any system, check the data plate information for maximum pressures allowed.

Leak testing methods

The *soap bubble test* is inexpensive and good for finding large leaks that have been localized in high-pressure systems. The flame of a *halide torch leak detector* changes color when halide is detected. An *electronic halide detector* uses an ionization cell to detect the presence of halides. These detectors are effective at detecting small leaks, but may be ineffective in the event of major leaks or background halides. The *ultrasonic leak detector* utilizes an ultrasonic sensor to "listen" for leaking gas. This method requires some advance knowledge of the location and a fairly low level of

Table 1 from EPA regulations

Type of appliance	Manufacture or import date of recycling equipment	
	Before Nov. 15, 1993	On or after Nov. 15, 1993
HCFC-22 appliance, or isolated component of such appliance, normally containing less than 200 lb of refrigerant	0	0
HCFC-22 appliance, or isolated component of such appliance, normally containing 200 lb or more of refrigerant	4	10
Very high-pressure appliance	0	0
Other high-pressure appliance, or isolated component of such appliance, normally containing less than 200 lb of refrigerant	4	10
Other high-pressure appliance, or isolated component of such appliance, normally containing more than 200 lb of refrigerant	4	15
Low-pressure appliance	25	25 mm Hg absolute (29 in. Hg)

Numbers represent inches of mercury vacuum relative to standard atmospheric pressure of 29.9 in. Hg, except where noted.

Required levels of evacuation for air conditioning, refrigeration, and recovery/recycling equipment

background noise. Since it depends strictly on the *sound* of the leaking gas, a system can be leak tested using a charge of dry nitrogen alone. This is considered to be the most environmentally safe technique, and is especially appropriate for newly installed systems before evacuation and charging with refrigerant.

Oil additives have also been developed for leak testing. Leaks are located by inspecting the unit with an ultraviolet (black) light and observing a fluorescent glow at the leak. This method is very effective on large equipment. The electronic and ultrasonic detectors are generally considered the most effective for locating the general area of small leaks.

General procedures   Once the system is pressurized, clean each area in which a leak is suspected. Remove all loose paint, insulation, rust, flux, weld slag, or thread sealant from any location where a detector probe may be placed. Clean up all oil, grease, and water. These substances can contaminate the sensing tip of a detector, causing it to fail or to give false indications. Vapor can flow along under a layer of paint and rust, or under pipe insulation, emerging at some distance from the actual leak.

An escaping gas is easier to detect if it is allowed to collect. Even slight air currents can dissipate leaking refrigerant. It may be necessary to drape the system area with a tarpaulin or plastic sheeting to block air currents.

When running the sensor over areas where leaks are suspected, remember that refrigerant is heavier than air. Check beneath seals, fittings, joints, valve covers, gaskets, etc. If a system has been idle for several months, the most likely leak site will be a shaft seal.

As refrigerant leaks out, it falls to the lowest point nearby. Check likely places of accumulation: evaporator drain pans, enclosed chassis, low cavities, etc. Move the sensor slowly enough for the presence of leaked vapor to register.

The final check for leaks is called the *standing vacuum test*, in which the system is evacuated and a deep vacuum is pulled on the system. An increase in pressure indicates a leak. ASHRAE Guideline 3-1990 recommends that if the pressure in a system rises from 1 mm Hg to 2.5 mm during a standing vacuum test, it should be checked for leaks.

Requirements for repair Units containing a refrigerant charge of 50 lb or more have very stringent rules regulating leak rates and leak repairs. Leaking industrial process refrigeration systems must be repaired if the leak rate is 35% or more of the charge in any 12-month period. The leak rate on all other types of systems is 15% or more of its total charge in any 12-month period.

DEHYDRATION

Filter-driers are used to control the circulation of moisture in a system. However, they are not designed to remove large amounts of moisture, which may enter a system during installation of the equipment, a major repair, or when the system is open for some other reason. A deep vacuum is necessary to remove this moisture. A good vacuum pump and vacuum gauge are required. The line connections should be the same size or larger than the vacuum pump connection, and as short as possible to minimize pressure drop. The finished vacuum is usually set for 1 mm (millimeter), which is equal to 1,000 microns. The system may be heated to decrease dehydration time (the size of the vacuum pump can govern the amount of time required to reach the desired level). Moisture remaining in an operating system can cause acid to form. A deep vacuum will remove only water vapor, not oil or acids.

REFRIGERANT SAFETY

The following are general safety considerations concerning fluorocarbon refrigerants. Before using or handling any refrigerant, personnel should be familiar with safety concerns for the specific product. This is particularly important for some of the new replacement refrigerants. Specific product safety information is available from the manufacturer.

Health hazards Although the toxicity of fluorocarbon refrigerants is low, the possibility of injury or death exists in unusual situations, or if they are deliberately misused. The vapors are several times heavier than air. Good ventilation must be provided in areas where high concentrations of the heavy vapors might accumulate and exclude oxygen.

Inhalation of concentrated refrigerant vapor is dangerous and can be fatal. Exposure to levels of fluorocarbons above recommended exposure levels can result in loss of concentration and drowsiness. There have been reported cases of fatal cardiac arrhythmia in humans accidentally exposed to high levels. Skin or eye contact can result in irritation and frostbite.

Note that exposure levels for some of the new replacement refrigerants are much lower than for those with which you may be familiar.

If cases of inhalation, remove the victim to fresh air. If the victim is not breathing, administer artificial respiration. If breathing is difficult, give oxygen. Avoid stimulants. Do *not* give adrenaline (epinephrine)—it can have potentially detrimental effects on the heart. Call a physician.

First aid   In cases of eye contact, flush eyes promptly with plenty of water for at least 15 minutes. Call a physician. Flush exposed skin with water (not hot) or use other means to warm skin slowly.

Other hazards   Most halogenated compounds decompose at high temperatures (such as those associated with gas flames or electric heaters). The chemicals that result under these circumstances always include hydrofluoric acid. If the compound contains chlorine, hydrochloric acid also will be formed and, if a source of water (or oxygen) is present, a smaller amount of phosgene. Fortunately, the halogen acids have a very sharp, stinging effect on the nose and can be detected by odor at concentrations below their toxic level. These acids serve as warning agents that decomposition has occurred. If they are detected, the area should be evacuated until the air has been cleared of decomposition products.

Precautions   Observe the following guidelines when working with or around refrigerants:

▶   Always read the product label and the product Material Safety Data Sheet (MSDS).

▶ Always use with adequate ventilation. Most fatal accidents involving refrigerant are due to oxygen deprivation.

▶ Never expose refrigerants to flames, sparks, or hot surfaces.

▶ Never trap liquid refrigerant between valves where there is no pressure relief device. A dirty pressure relief device must be replaced.

▶ Use an alcohol spray to clean refrigerant sight glasses that have become coated with ice.

▶ When leak testing a system, use nitrogen for increasing the pressure after the refrigerant is recovered. Use a pressure regulator on the nitrogen cylinder to ensure a safe pressure in the system. The low-side test pressure value listed on the data plate should be used as the maximum pressure applied to the system for leak testing.

▶ Never use oxygen or compressed air for pressurization— some refrigerants may explode when under pressure and mixed with air.

▶ Physicians: Do not use epinephrine to treat overexposure.

Safety equipment

Personnel handling refrigerants should wear side-shield safety glasses, impervious (preferably butyl-lined) gloves, and other protective equipment or clothing as required by the employer or the situation.

Auxiliary breathing apparatus should be readily accessible in storage, handling, and production areas in case an abnormally high concentration of refrigerant vapor should develop. Showers and eyewash fountains of the deluge type should be readily accessible in case of contact with the skin or eyes.

ASHRAE Standard 34

ASHRAE has developed a safety classification matrix for refrigerants based on toxicity and flammability ratings. *Toxicity* ratings are based on a TLV/TWA index. "TLV" stands for *threshold limit value* (exposure of 8 to 12 hr per day, 5 days a week, for 40 years), and "TWA" stands for *time-weighted average*

(average exposure expressed in hours per day). Refrigerants are assigned to one of two classes, depending on the allowable exposure:

▶ Class A: TLV/TWA of 400 ppm or greater

▶ Class B: TLV/TWA of 399 ppm or less

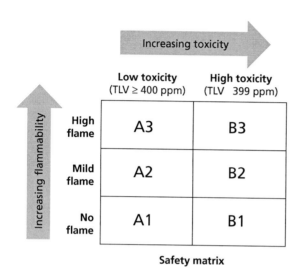

Safety matrix

Flammability also is rated:

▶ Class 1: *no* flame propagation

▶ Class 2: *low* flame propagation

▶ Class 3: *high* flame propagation

Refrigerants can then be classified according to a matrix, as shown in the illustration above. As you can see, an "A1" rating denotes the safest refrigerants to handle, and "B3" the most dangerous. Of the refrigerants now commonly in use or coming into use as replacements, most are classified as A1 (but note that R–123 is B1).

REFRIGERANT CYLINDERS

Disposable cylinders

Refrigerants are usually packaged in disposable containers for use by air conditioning and refrigeration service personnel. Disposable cylinders are manufactured in three sizes: 20-lb, 30-lb, and 50-lb capacities. The 20-lb size is the *minimum* size cylinder that can be purchased legally by technicians who are certified only under Section 608. (Smaller sizes are available to MVAC technicians certified under Section 609.)

Refrigerant manufacturers and packagers voluntarily color-code cylinders for their chlorofluorocarbon products. Note that the shade of color may vary somewhat between manufacturers.

Refrigerant cylinder color codes

Refrigerant	Color	PMS #
R-11	Orange	021
R-12	White	White
R-13	Light blue	2975
R-22	Light green	352
R-113	Dark purple	266
R-114	Dark blue	302
R-123	Light blue gray	428
R-124	Deep green	335
R-125	Medium brown	465
R-134a	Light blue	2975
R-401A	Light pink	177
R-401B	Yellow brown	124
R-402A	Light brown	461
R-402B	Green brown	385
R-404A	Orange	021
R-410A	Deep pink	507
R-500	Yellow	109

Colors are per ARI Guideline N. Please refer to Pantone® Matching System (PMS) color formula guide for exact color match.

Regulations

Disposable cylinders are manufactured to specifications established by the U.S. Department of Transportation (DOT), which has regulatory authority over all hazardous materials in commercial transportation. Disposable cylinders must adhere to Specification 39. One-trip cylinders, therefore, are often referred to as "DOT-39s" (see illustration next page).

All cylinders used for CFCs are manufactured to handle R-502, the refrigerant with the highest operating pressure. Disposable cylinders for R-502 must be rated for a service pressure of 260 psi. DOT Specification 39 stipulates that cylinders with a 260-psi service pressure must be leak tested at 325 psi. One cylinder per thousand is pressurized to the point of failure. The cylinder must not rupture below 650 psi. These tests are intended to assure that users receive safe and leak-free containers.

Safety relief devices

Every cylinder is equipped with a safety relief device that will vent pressure from the cylinder before it reaches the rupture point. Two versions are approved for DOT-39 cylinders. The most common is a frangible disk, typically welded to the cylinder shoulder. If cylinder pressure exceeds 340 psi, the coin will burst and the cylinder's contents will be vented, thus preventing an explosion.

The second design is a spring-loaded relief integrated in the valve stem. When the cylinder's internal pressure exceeds 340 psi, the pressure forces the spring to open, venting a portion of the cylinder's contents through the relief port.

DOT-39 disposable cylinder

Cylinders can become overpressurized for several reasons, primarily overheating. When temperatures rise, the compressed gas expands and can liquid-fill the cylinder. This is known as a *hydrostatic* condition. When a cylinder reaches a hydrostatic condition, the internal pressure rises very rapidly with even minor increases in temperature. If the safety relief device is unable to vent the increased pressure adequately, the cylinder could explode, causing property damage, personal injury, or even death. *Never* tamper with a cylinder safety device, or overfill a cylinder.

A cylinder also can become overpressurized if it is connected to the discharge side of a refrigeration or air conditioning system. In such cases, the compressor can create pressures greater than the capacity of the safety relief device on the cylinder.

Hazards of reuse

Disposable cylinders are manufactured from steel. Rust can eventually weaken the cylinder to the point at which the wall can no longer contain the compressed gas. Cylinders must be stored and transported in dry environments. Cylinders exhibiting extreme rust should be emptied of their contents and properly discarded.

Every refrigerant cylinder is silk-screened with product, safety, and warning information. This information, as well as information available in manufacturer's technical bulletins and the product's Material Safety Data Sheet (MSDS), should be read carefully and followed.

Manufacturers of DOT-39 cylinders have switched to a one-way valve design, which allows the refrigerant to be removed, but prevents the cylinder from being refilled. A green valve handle identifies these newer cylinders (older cylinders had a black valve handle). Transportation of refilled DOT-39 cylinders is illegal and subject to a penalty of up to $25,000 in fines and five years of imprisonment.

Disposal   All refrigerants should be properly recovered from empty disposable cylinders. The cylinder can be punctured with the valve open. Used cylinders can be recycled with your scrap metal dealer. Never leave used cylinders with residual product outdoors or at a job site. The internal pressure of a cylinder containing one ounce of liquid refrigerant is exactly the same as that of a full cylinder. An abandoned cylinder will eventually deteriorate—and potentially rupture if the cylinder wall weakens before the safety device activates.

Safety guidelines   The following safety guidelines apply to *all* cylinders:

▶ *Never* drop a cylinder, or hit it with a hammer or any other tool.

▶ *Never* apply live steam or direct flame to a cylinder.

▶ Do not lift a cylinder by its valve cover or valve. Never remove a valve from a cylinder, or attempt to repair it.

▶ Do not tamper with the cylinder's safety device.

▶ *Never* refill disposable cylinders.

▶ Do not remove or attempt to alter any permanent cylinder markings (it is illegal to do so).

▶ Be careful not to dent, cut, or scratch any cylinder or valve.

▶ Protect cylinders from moisture, salt, and corrosive chemicals or a corrosive atmosphere, in any form.

▶ Always open valves slowly, and close after each use.

▶ Do not attempt to use a cylinder in a rusted or otherwise deteriorated condition. Contact appropriate personnel for disposal.

Handling guidelines

Except for drums of R-11, R-113, R-123, and disposable and service cylinders, almost all refrigerant cylinders are deposit containers. The manufacturer of the refrigerant usually retains ownership of these cylinders. The use of such cylinders for any purpose other than the removal of the original refrigerant is generally prohibited. A service technician or contractor must obtain a formal waiver from the manufacturer to use these cylinders for other purposes, including the storage of used or contaminated refrigerant or the recycling or reclaiming of refrigerant.

Disposable cylinders may be used for shipping virgin refrigerant only. They are never permitted for any further use.

OSHA (Occupational Safety and Health Administration) requires that compressed gas cylinders be used *only* by individuals who are trained in the proper handling and safe use of such cylinders.

Never mix one refrigerant with another type of refrigerant. Many common refrigerants, such as R-12 and R-22, form azeotropes with other refrigerants. These mixtures may be impossible to separate, and consequently must be destroyed rather than reclaimed.

Use personal protective equipment when filling and handling cylinders. This includes side-shield glasses, gloves, and safety shoes. Avoid skin contact with liquid refrigerant.

Be aware that inhaling high concentrations of any refrigerant vapor is harmful. It may cause heart irregularities, loss of consciousness, or death. Since vapor is heavier than air, avoid low areas without suitable ventilation. *Always exercise extreme caution when moving cylinders.*

Recovery cylinders

Recovery cylinders must comply with DOT specifications. Small (30-lb and 50-lb) recovery cylinders are painted yellow in the shoulder area and 12 in. down the side. The remainder of the cylinder body is painted gray. Use only recovery cylinders that are identified for used refrigerant. Do *not* use cylinders designed for virgin refrigerant.

Filling the cylinder

Prior to filling a cylinder, inspect it for signs of damage. Look for dents or corrosion. Do not fill a damaged cylinder. Do not fill a recovery cylinder that is out of date. The present date cannot be more than five years past the test date stamped on the shoulder of the cylinder. The test date will look something like this:

A1
12   **89**
32

The designation in this example tells you that the cylinder was retested in December 1989 by retester number A132. If a cylinder is out of date—as the one in the example above would be after December 1994—it must *not* be filled. Promptly return it to the cylinder owner for retesting.

Liquefied used refrigerant expands when exposed to high temperatures. If the cylinder is overfilled, thermal expansion of the liquid can rupture the cylinder.

After filling, it is important to verify that all cylinder valves are closed properly. This prevents leaks during subsequent handling and shipment. If necessary, leak test the valves using soapy water.

Shipping procedures

The EPA does not characterize used refrigerants as hazardous waste. Most states share this view and, as a result, require no special procedures for used refrigerant shipments. However, several states have their own waste classification for used refrigerants. These states may require special shipping procedures. If a shipment originates in any of these states, the shipper should contact the appropriate agency to determine whether special shipping instructions apply. The following information is *not* complete for shipping used refrigerants that are classified as hazardous waste.

The reclaimer you select will be able to supply you with specific information on shipping your recovered refrigerant. Most will also supply the required labels and forms. All used refrigerant containers must be properly labeled. Cylinders and drums should be labeled *prior* to filling. Never fill a cylinder or drum that is not labeled for that material. Unlabeled containers in your truck could be dangerous and illegal. In the event of an accident, most emergency personnel are instructed to avoid unidentified containers or cylinders. They must wait for a hazardous materials response team to arrive and identify the contents of the containers. This can cause unnecessary delays.

The following is a summary of typical requirements and procedures: Apply the appropriate *used refrigerant label* to the shoulder of each cylinder. If the label on the cylinder is illegible, remove it completely and apply a new label. The CAS (Chemical Abstracts Service) number and UN/NA (United Nations/North American) identification number must always be shown. Next, install the gold hood cap over the cylinder valve. Complete a *used refrigerant identification tag* for each cylinder. Attach this tag to the gold hood cap with a plastic tie. Complete a green DOT *classification tag* for each cylinder. Attach the tag to the gold hood cap with a plastic tie. Finally, complete the bill of lading. The following information generally is required:

▶ Company name of carrier

▶ Date

▶ Company name and address of shipper

▶ Signature of shipping company's representative

▶ Shipping destination

- Identity of refrigerant (R-12, R-22, etc.) and UN/NA number

- Type and size of container (cylinders, drums, ton tanks, etc.)

- Number of containers being shipped

- Gross product weight, in pounds

- Shipping information

The illustration below shows an example of a used R-12 label, and of a used refrigerant identification tag.

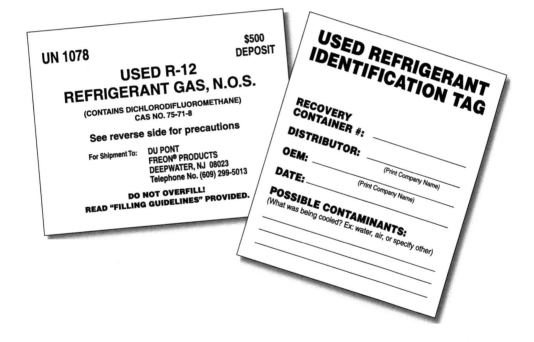

Section 2

SMALL APPLIANCES

THE TYPE I SECTION OF THIS STUDY GUIDE is designed to help technicians understand the information necessary for obtaining Type I certification. The Type I classification certifies technicians for refrigerant service of small appliances. The EPA defines a small appliance as any of the following:

> *Appliances that are fully manufactured, charged, and hermetically sealed in a factory with 5 lb or less of refrigerant: home refrigerators and freezers, room air conditioners (including window units and packaged terminal air conditioners), packaged terminal heat pumps, dehumidifiers, under-the-counter ice makers, vending machines, and drinking water coolers.*

It is recommended that this section be studied if you are attempting a Universal certification, or if you are taking or retaking the Type I exam. Many of the questions for the Type I exam cover information that comes from the Core section of this book. But in addition to relevant material from the Core section, you should study the following information, which is unique to Type I.

The EPA definition of a "small" appliance quoted on the previous page limits the type of equipment included in Type I certification. Central air conditioning systems, MVAC-like equipment, and commercial refrigeration equipment are *not* included in Type I, even though they may contain less than 5 lb of refrigerant. A few further definitions may be helpful at this point:

▶ **Appliance.** Any device that contains and uses a Class I (CFC) or Class II (HCFC) substance as a refrigerant, and which is used for household or commercial purposes, including any air conditioner, refrigerator, chiller, or freezer.

▶ **MVAC-like appliance.** Any mechanical vapor compression, open-drive compressor appliance used to cool the driver's or passenger's compartment of a non-road motor vehicle. Includes the air conditioning equipment in agriculture and construction vehicles. This definition is not intended to cover appliances using HCFC-22.

▶ **Technician.** Any person who performs maintenance, service, or repair that could reasonably be expected to release refrigerant to the atmosphere. Includes, but is not limited to, installers, contractor employees, in-house service personnel, and sometimes owners. Also includes any person disposing of appliances except small appliances.

▶ **Major maintenance, service, or repair.** Any service involving the removal of any or all of the following components: compressor, condenser, evaporator, or auxiliary heat exchanger coil.

It is important to note the reference to the system being "hermetically sealed." Small appliance systems do not require service connections, but must have some type of service aperture. This usually takes the form of a straight piece of tubing (process tube), which can be used for connection with piercing access valves. Access valves must be checked for leaks after they have been installed and before the refrigerant has been recovered. These valves must be removed after repairs are completed and before recharging takes place, since they have a tendency to leak after a period of equipment operation.

Appliances should be checked visually for leaks (look for any sign of oil) before you start the recovery process. If the gauges read 0 psig (atmospheric pressure) when initially connected to the system, do not attempt to recover any refrigerant. Doing so will only pump noncondensables into the recovery vessel.

RECOVERY

Before beginning a refrigerant recovery procedure, *always* make sure to identify the refrigerant that you are about to recover. Some older refrigerators or freezers may contain non-fluorocarbon refrigerants, which must not be recovered with current recovery equipment. The same is true for many recreational vehicle appliances, both old and new.

Recovery of refrigerant from a small appliance may be accomplished in either of two ways—with system-dependent recovery equipment, or with self-contained recovery equipment.

System-dependent recovery equipment requires the assistance of components contained within the appliance to remove the refrigerant. The refrigerant must be recovered into a non-pressurized container, such as a specifically designed heavy-mil plastic bag. *Never* use a vacuum pump for any type of refrigerant recovery. A vacuum pump only pumps vapor at atmospheric pressure or lower.

Self-contained recovery equipment is equipment capable of removing the refrigerant from an appliance without the assistance of components contained within the appliance.

Techniques A recovery cylinder should be evacuated to 1,000 microns before initial use. *Never* mix refrigerants in the same cylinder. You must allow a cylinder to reach a known (room) temperature before you can obtain an accurate pressure reading. Once you know the temperature-pressure relationship, you will be able to tell whether excessive air or other non-condensables are present in the cylinder.

Remember: *Always* verify the type of refrigerant in the appliance. R-134A is the refrigerant used in new domestic refrigerators and freezers. At present, there is no "drop-in" refrigerant that can be used as a replacement for R-12. R-12 must be completely recovered before any other refrigerant can be installed.

Requirements When recovering refrigerant with system-dependent equipment, you must be able to recover 80% of the charge if the compressor is not operating. Recover the refrigerant from both the high and low sides of the system. This will ensure complete recovery and speed the process. Warming the compressor oil and tapping the compressor with a rubber hammer will help release refrigerant from the oil. Energizing the defrost heaters on a frost-free refrigerator or freezer can decrease recovery time. If the compressor is operating, 90% of the charge must be recovered. Run the compressor and recover the refrigerant from the high side.

When recovering refrigerant with self-contained equipment, you must evacuate the system to a 4-in. vacuum. This type of equipment, if manufactured after November 15, 1993, must have low-loss fittings and be certified by an EPA-approved third party. Low-loss fittings can be manually closed or close automatically when disconnected.

REFRIGERATION CYCLE

The diagram on page 30 in the Core section of this book illustrates a basic refrigeration cycle. Be aware that a small appliance as defined under Type I classification does not use a receiver or the type of suction accumulator shown. The normal high-side connection for a small appliance is a process tube at the outlet of the condenser. The normal low-side connection is a low-pressure process tube on the hermetic compressor, or the suction line close to the compressor.

SAFETY

When you are recovering refrigerants, safety goggles or glasses and butyl-lined gloves are necessary attire. Nitrogen is the recommended inert gas for leak checking a system. An HCFC refrigerant, preferably R-22, should be used as a trace gas. A regulator must be used on the nitrogen cylinder to control the amount of pressure applied to the appliance.

Because refrigerants are heavier than air, a large leak or accidental release of refrigerant can deplete the oxygen level in the work area. The area should be evacuated immediately and ventilated. High temperatures, normally from an open flame, can cause the refrigerant to decompose, forming hydrofluoric and hydrochloric acids and phosgene gas. Before using cylinders that are equipped with Schrader valves, inspect any such valve for a damaged core. Make sure that a cap is installed whenever connections are not applied.

Charging cylinders with graduated markings normally are filled with liquid at the valve connection located at the lowest point (bottom) of the cylinder. The vapor released from the upper (top) valve connection must be recovered. The release of vapor to the atmosphere is prohibited.

Section 3

HIGH-PRESSURE SYSTEMS

THE TYPE II SECTION OF THIS STUDY GUIDE is designed to help technicians understand the information necessary for obtaining Type II certification. The Type II classification certifies technicians for refrigerant service of high-pressure and very high-pressure appliances. The EPA defines a high-pressure appliance as:

> *Any appliance that uses a refrigerant with a boiling point between −50 and +10°C (between −58 and +50°F) at atmospheric pressure (29.92 in. Hg). Includes, but is not limited to, R-12, R-22, R-114, R-500, and R-502.*

The EPA defines a very high-pressure appliance as:

> *Any appliance that uses a refrigerant with a boiling point below −50°C (−58°F) at atmospheric pressure (29.92 in. Hg). Includes, but is not limited to, R-13 and R-503.*

It is recommended that this section be studied if you are attempting a Universal certification, or if you are taking or retaking the Type II exam. Many of the questions for the Type II exam cover information that comes from the Core section of this book. But in addition to relevant material from the Core section, you should study the following information, which is unique to Type II.

LEAK DETECTION

All high-pressure or very high-pressure appliances should be visually inspected for signs of oil when a leak is suspected. (Oil travels through the system with the refrigerant, and will leave traces wherever a large enough leak is present). The Core section of this book describes the various methods of leak detection (soap bubbles, electronic, ultrasonic, and dye) that have been approved by the EPA.

Open compressors used in the HVACR industry have an inherent tendency to leak at the shaft seal if the system has not been run for a long period of time. Excessive superheat on the suction side of the system is an indication of a leak. When the use of an inert gas (nitrogen) is not sufficient for leak testing, a small amount of an HCFC refrigerant (preferably R-22) may be added to the appliance as a trace gas.

Repair requirements

EPA regulations require all appliances containing 50 lb or more of refrigerant (except commercial and industrial process refrigeration) to be repaired if the leak rate exceeds 15% of the total charge per year. Commercial and industrial process refrigeration must be repaired if the leak rate exceeds 35% of the total charge per year.

RECOVERY

Techniques

It is important for maintenance to be performed periodically on recovery machines. Oil and filters should be changed at properly scheduled intervals. Most small recovery units have air-cooled condensers that should be clean at all times. Larger recovery machines may have water-cooled condensers. The water supply for these condensers must be obtained from a local municipal source, not from the equipment. Any refrigerant left in the machine from the last recovery job must be recovered before connecting the machine to another appliance. The refillable cylinder must be evacuated, with a vacuum pump, prior to the recovery process.

The fastest method of recovery is to remove as much refrigerant as possible in the liquid phase. It is possible that some oil will be removed along with the liquid refrigerant. Inspect the system first in order to locate the proper place for the removal of liquid refrigerant. The liquid line is generally the proper connection point. However, if the condenser is located below the evaporator or receiver, the connection should be at the condenser outlet. If the condenser is above the evaporator, recovery should begin from the liquid line entering the evaporator.

The vapor remaining in the appliance must be recovered after the liquid refrigerant has been removed. Recovery time can be reduced by packing the recovery cylinder in ice. Recovery equipment that uses a hermetic compressor as the pump may shut down before completing the process, due to overheating of the compressor motor. Superheat in the vapor may prevent the vapor from cooling the motor. If you consistently work on larger equipment, a recovery machine that uses an oil-less compressor may be a wise investment. The refrigerant in a system that includes a receiver may be recovered into the receiver when service is being performing on other portions of the unit.

Requirements   EPA regulations governing recovery equipment and vacuum standards are summarized in Table 1 on page 43. It is imperative that service technicians who perform recovery procedures adhere to these regulations. As you can see, Table 1 shows acceptable vacuum levels according to the type of refrigerant and the amount of refrigerant in a system. (Leak regulations change at the 50-lb charge level and vacuum regulations change at the 200-lb charge level.) The date of manufacture of the recovery equipment determines the vacuum level that it must be capable of achieving. When an appliance has a leak, it can be evacuated to atmospheric pressure (0 psig). System-dependent recovery equipment cannot be used on an appliance that contains more than 15 lb of refrigerant.

REFRIGERATION CYCLE

The diagram on page 30 in the Core section of this book shows the major components of a high-pressure appliance (compressor, condenser, metering device, evaporator), plus a receiver and an accumulator. The location and function of each component are considered required knowledge for a HVACR service technician.

The receiver is located in the high side of the system when the metering device is a thermostatic expansion valve. A receiver is not used when the metering device is a capillary tube or fixed orifice. The refrigerant leaving the receiver is high-pressure liquid. The accumulator is located in the low side to collect any liquid refrigerant that may leave the evaporator, thus protecting the compressor. A heater located in the crankcase of the compressor is designed to reduce the amount of refrigerant in the lubricating oil. An excessive amount of refrigerant in the oil can cause oil foaming in the crankcase and a loss of lubrication to the compressor parts. Many of the service valves installed on these appliances are double-seating valves. The technician must be able to identify the direction of flow when the service valve stem is in a particular position.

A vacuum pump used to remove moisture and non-condensables from an appliance after repair should be capable of pulling a vacuum of at least 500 microns. It is possible that too large a vacuum pump may be used on an appliance. If this happens, the vacuum may reach the point at which water will freeze in the appliance before it can be removed. This will greatly increase the time needed to reach the desired vacuum. Be especially careful when you recharge systems that contain water-cooled condensers or chiller-type evaporators. After vapor has been added to increase the pressure of a given refrigerant above 32°F (36°F generally is recommended), the system can be charged with liquid through the liquid-line service valve. It is important to keep the circulating pumps of the water circuit running during the charging operation.

SAFETY

You should follow general safety practices, as covered in the Core section of this book, when performing service on any appliance. But be aware that many of the systems covered by Type II are very large, and have different safety demands than small appliances do. The reciprocating compressors used on larger equipment may have service valves on both the suction and the discharge sides. The discharge-side service valve should never be front-seated while the compressor is in operation. The receiver of a Type II system must have a pressure relief device on it. These relief devices should never be connected in series. Sight glasses and viewing glasses may become covered with ice. An alcohol spray should be used to remove this ice (not a screwdriver!). Remember: *Think safety!*

Section 4

LOW-PRESSURE SYSTEMS

THE TYPE III SECTION OF THIS STUDY GUIDE is designed to help technicians understand the information necessary for obtaining Type III certification. The Type III classification certifies technicians for refrigerant service of low–pressure appliances (centrifugal chillers). The EPA defines a low–pressure appliance as:

> *Any appliance that uses a refrigerant with a boiling point above 10°C (50°F) at atmospheric pressure (29.92 in. Hg). Includes, but is not limited to, R-11, R-113, and R-123.*

It is recommended that this section be studied if you are attempting a Universal certification, or you are taking or retaking the Type III exam. Many of the questions for the Type III exam cover information that comes from the Core section of this book. But in addition to relevant material from the Core section, you should study the following information, which is unique to Type III.

LEAK DETECTION

Leak testing low-pressure systems involves considerations not present in equipment designed to operate at higher pressures. The EPA requires all commercial and industrial process refrigeration systems containing more than 50 lb of refrigerant to be repaired if the leak rate exceeds 35% of the total charge per year. All other types of systems containing more than 50 lb of refrigerant must be repaired if the leak rate exceeds 15% of the total charge per year.

ASHRAE Guideline 3 states that a system should be checked for leaks if, during a standing vacuum test beginning at 1 mm Hg, the pressure rises to above 2.5 mm Hg.

Tubes in a low-pressure system may be checked for leaks using a hydrostatic tube test kit.

Low-pressure systems are protected against overpressure by a rupture disk at the evaporator. The rupture disk is designed to relieve pressure at 15 psig. Never raise the pressure beyond 10 psig, or the rupture disk could fail.

The best method of raising system pressure for leak testing is to raise the temperature carefully—for example, by circulating controlled-temperature hot water. Heat blanket systems (PREVAC) that serve the purpose are also available.

Purge units are necessary on low-pressure systems because the low side operates below atmospheric pressure and can draw in air (a noncondensable), mostly at gaskets and fittings. Leaks in the system admit more air, causing excessive operation of the purge system. When the purge operates, a small amount of refrigerant is also discharged. To reduce this loss, the chiller should be leak tested and repaired as necessary. Excessive moisture collection in the purge unit can indicate a leak in the condenser or chiller barrel tubes.

The shell-and-tube evaporator (the "cooler") of a water chiller is where cooling takes place. Heat is absorbed by refrigerant in the shell, chilling the water flowing through the tubes. The tubes are secured into a tube sheet at each end. Water is supplied to the tubes, and collected from them, via cavities formed between the tube sheets and outside header caps. These cavities are called "water boxes." When the chiller is operating, any leak in the water tubes will cause water to leak from the tube into the shell. However, if the water flow is valved off and the water is drained, refrigerant in the shell will pass through the leak into the tubes, and will collect in the water boxes. Refrigerant then can be detected by inserting a leak detector probe through the drain valve in either of the water boxes.

RECOVERY

Techniques
The high-pressure cut-out on a recovery unit must be set at 10 psig when you are removing refrigerant from a low-pressure chiller (the low-pressure recovery vessel rupture disk relieves at 15 psig).

Recover liquid refrigerant first, then vapor. Removing the vapor after liquid recovery has been performed is important: a 350-ton R-11 chiller at 0 psig could still contain 100 lb of refrigerant in vapor form, even after the liquid refrigerant has been removed.

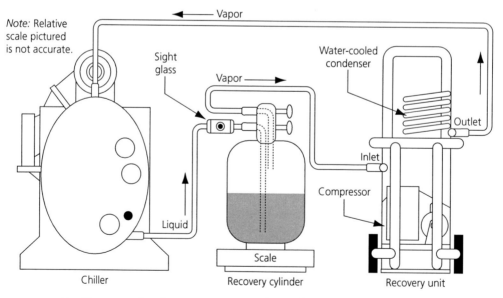

Liquid recovery from low-pressure system (type of recovery container may vary)

Heat can be used as a tool in recovering or recharging refrigerant in a low-pressure system. Oil will contain less refrigerant at higher temperatures (130 to 140°F suggested). When recovering refrigerant from chillers, remember to maintain water circulation to prevent freezing. In the case of a water-cooled recovery unit, this means that when vapor is being removed, the recovery unit's condenser water (usually from the municipal water supply) and the condenser and chilled water system pumps *all* should be on while the recovery pump is running.

Requirements EPA regulations include very specific requirements regarding the recovery of refrigerant from low-pressure systems. After the refrigerant removal procedure has been completed and the required recovery vacuum has been reached, some refrigerant could still exist in the system or in the oil. Wait at least a few minutes and check the system pressure for any rise, which could indicate that further recovery is necessary to attain the required evacuation level.

Systems do not need to be evacuated all the way to the required level if either of the following conditions applies:

▶ The service procedure does not qualify as "major" (see definition on page 59).

▶ Because of leaks, evacuation to the required level cannot be attained or would contaminate the refrigerant being recovered.

In the first case—that of a non-"major" repair—the low-pressure system must be pressurized to 0 psig using a method such as controlled hot water, *not* a method that would require subsequent purging, such as adding nitrogen.

Recovery and recycling equipment manufactured after November 15, 1993 must be tested by an EPA-approved third party, and must be equipped with low-loss fittings. Be aware, too, that the vacuum levels required for service or disposal vary according to the date of manufacture of the equipment being used. If you are using equipment that was manufactured *before*

November 15, 1993, you must evacuate low-pressure systems to 25 in. Hg. If you are using equipment manufactured *after* that date, the required vacuum is 25 mm absolute (approximately 29 in. Hg).

RECHARGING TECHNIQUES

Since large low-pressure systems are designed to chill water, charging methods must take the presence of water into consideration. Introducing liquid into a deep vacuum can cause the refrigerant to boil, and may lower temperatures enough to freeze water in the tubes. After service or repair of a low-pressure system, therefore, always charge in the *vapor* phase until the refrigerant saturation temperature increases to 36°F. After that point, you may begin charging liquid refrigerant. A temperature-pressure chart should be used to determine the pressure for the refrigerant being charged (see the T-P chart on page 34 in the Core section).

The recovery vessel being used to charge the vapor can be warmed with a heat blanket to increase the flow into the repaired system. The lowest access point on a low-pressure system is the evaporator charging valve.

REFRIGERATION CYCLE

Because it operates at a pressure below atmospheric, a low-pressure system requires a purge unit to remove noncondensables from the system. The purge unit draws (takes its suction) from the top of the condenser and returns the refrigerant to the evaporator.

When a low-pressure system is idle for a long period of time, the system pressure should be maintained at a level slightly higher than atmospheric. The presence of air in an operating system normally is indicated by a higher-than-normal head pressure. If you use a vacuum pump that is too large, the pressure may drop so rapidly that water trapped in the system will freeze. If a smaller vacuum pump is not available, you may be able to use nitrogen with a regulator to increase the pressure enough to control this condition.

Since low-pressure refrigerants remain in liquid form at atmospheric pressure and relatively high temperatures, specific safety precautions must be observed. *Never* attempt to siphon refrigerant by mouth, and avoid spilling it on exposed skin. Observe all requirements for safe handling, including the use of non-permeable gloves and eye protection (glasses or goggles) when working with refrigerants.

Precautions for the safety of the system also must be observed. Never install pressure relief valves in series. If ice forms on the outside of the system sight glass(es), remove it with an alcohol spray. Do *not* scrape or chip ice away with any tool. The rupture disk in the evaporator is set to open at 15 psig. The discharge of this disk should be piped to the outdoors, not to anywhere inside the building.

The HVACR Training Authority

1666 Rand Road   Des Plaines, IL 60016   800-297-5660   www.rses.org